Chefables Presents

Chef Able's
Fables

Mouth-watering tales
with nutritious morals

Who is Chefables

Chefables is on a mission to cultivate healthy young eaters by providing meals that taste great and are good for you, not to mention compliant. We deliver fresh, innovative meals to preschools, childcare centers, and schools.

Please visit us at
www.chefables.com

ISBN: 978-0-9836626-0-0 (hardback)
ISBN: 978-0-9836626-1-7 (paperback)
First Printing

Dedicated to our loyal customers and
families with children everywhere.

Contents

The First Ever Recorded Non-Fiction Fairy Tale

Once upon a land, in a time not so far away,
there were two regular people named Kenny and Lesley.
Now, Kenny and Lesley had no hidden super powers, no wishes
to grant, and no magic dust to sprinkle. They didn't go around
kissing frogs, had no interest in poisonous apples and preferred
shag carpets to the magic ones. But what they lacked in fairy tale
endowments they made up for in passion, talent and drive. And when
they put those ingredients together…well, something fairy tale like
really did happen…they created Chefables. A company whose
mission is to cultivate healthy young eaters by providing
meals that taste great and are good for you.

So, Kenny put his culinary talents to the test by creating healthy,
delicious foods for the ficklest, pickiest eaters on the planet—kids.
While Lesley put her business smarts and customer service skills
to work by educating preschools, childcare centers, and schools
about the importance of developing healthy eating habits in kids.
Together this dynamic duo delivered yummy, well prepared,
meals to schools and centers all over the land. And all quite
affordably, conveniently, and compliantly.

Today, happy kids can be seen eating delicious dishes like
braised carrots, teriyaki salmon and homemade Fuji applesauce,
and often even asking for more. Which is why we need to
repeat a fact that was not so clearly stated but certainly insinuated
at the beginning of this story…this is not a typical fairy tale…
this, my dear reader, is all true.

Moral of the story: Chefables is on a mission to cultivate healthy young eaters by providing meals that taste great and are good for you, not to mention compliant.

THE RULE of THUMB

Meet John Q. Thumb, ruler of a great and powerful empire. John loved making rules. All kinds of rules. Good rules. Simple rules. Like don't talk with food in your mouth. Or don't run with scissors. But, his most important rule was to eat a well-balanced diet. It was so famous that it became known far and wide as the Rule of Thumb.

At any rate, everyone in the empire followed all the rules. And life was quiet, peaceful, and healthy in his empire…until one day when his evil twin, Jack showed up.

Now, Jack was just like John in every way. Except for one…John made rules and Jack broke them. As the story goes, right before John went away to the annual summer summit, he created Rule of Thumb proclamations that could be seen throughout the empire. John knew that if the people followed these rules they would be happy and healthy.

As soon as John was gone his brother Jack appeared with an evil smile in one hand and a big black marker in the other. He changed the Rule of Thumb to say: Don't eat a balanced meal. When John returned to his empire, he found all the people had become overweight and overtired. Especially, the children.

"What has happened to my people?" Thumb cried out. And then he noticed how his proclamations had been changed.

He knew this was the handiwork of his brother.

So, he searched the empire from top to bottom until he found Jack (who by the way was pretty easy to find since he had become so big he couldn't really hide at all.)

He banished Jack from the empire. Then he put his people back on a balanced diet. And everyone lived happily and healthily ever after.

MORAL of the STORY:

EATING A WELL BALANCED DIET IS THE BEST WAY TO PREVENT CHILDHOOD OBESITY.

AT CHEFABLES, WE MAKE SURE KIDS EAT WELL AND EAT RIGHT. BY PROVIDING SOUND NUTRITION IN PRESCHOOL, WE'RE HELPING PREVENT CHILDHOOD OBESITY, TYPE 2 DIABETES AND HEART DISEASE. ♔

C. Hale

THE ADVENTURES OF
CAPTAIN CAROTENE!

THE
ADVENTURES
OF

THE ADVENTURES OF CAPTAIN CAROTENE!

FRANK WAS A TYPICAL 5-YEAR OLD KID. HE LIKED PLAYING, DRAWING AND WATCHING CARTOONS. BUT, HE DIDN'T LIKE EATING HIS VEGETABLES.

TRY THIS, FRANK.

ONE DAY, HIS MOM MADE HIM A YUMMY CARROT CASSEROLE THINGY.

FIRST HE GLARED AT IT.

THEN HE STARED AT IT.

AND THEN FINALLY AFTER CAREFUL EXAMINATION HE TOOK A SMALL BITE.

HMM, THIS TASTES PRETTY GOOD.

CHEW CHEW

AFTER HE TOOK A FEW MORE BITES, WEIRD THINGS STARTED HAPPENING. LIKE HE BEGAN TO TURN BRIGHT ORANGE. NEXT WAVES OF GREEN POPPED OUT OF HIS HEAD. AND THEN WITHOUT WARNING OR PROVOCATION HE WAS WEARING A FORM FITTING UNITARD, SPACE BOOTS AND CAPE.

WHAT'S HAPPENING TO ME?

LUCKILY, THERE WAS A TALL BOTTLE OF H2O AND A LONE BRUSSEL SPROUT CHATTING NEARBY.

HEY, YOU'VE BEEN TRANSFORMED INTO CAPTAIN CAROTENE!

GOLLY, DOES THAT MEAN I'M A SUPER HERO? WHAT ARE MY SUPER POWERS? CAN I FLY? CAN I TURN INVISIBLE? CAN I CHANGE SHAPES? CAN I CROSS DIMENSIONS? CAN I BREAK THROUGH TO THE FOURTH WALL?

YOUR SPECIAL POWER IS THE ABILITY TO SEE INTO THE FUTURE!

WHICH WOULD BE PARTICULARLY USEFUL SINCE HE WOULD NEED IT TO PREVENT THE EVIL DR. FRY AND NURSE BATTER FROM TAKING OVER THE WORLD AND FRYING IT UP!

WELL, THE FUTURE ARRIVED EARLY ONE MORNING, WHILE CAPTAIN CAROTENE WAS CLEANING HIS VPS (VEGETABLE POSITIONING SYSTEM), BECAUSE THAT IS THE EXACT MOMENT HE SPOTTED THE EVIL DUO, HEADING TOWARDS A PRESCHOOL WITH BAGS AND BAGS OF SMILEY MEALS.

HERE THEY GO AGAIN TRYING TO CONVINCE KIDS THAT EATING FRIED FOODS IS BETTER TASTING AND BETTER FOR THEM THAN EATING WELL COOKED HEALTHY MEALS.

CAPTAIN CAROTENE IMMEDIATELY GRABBED HIS ANTI-FRYING FRYING PAN AND BLASTED THEM OFF COURSE.

ONCE AGAIN, THE WORLD IS NOW SAFE FOR WELL-PREPARED NUTRITIOUS AND DELICIOUS MEALS LIKE THE ONES YOU CAN GET FROM CHEFABLES.

AS FOR DR. FRY AND NURSE BATTER THEY WERE LAST SEEN WANDERING AIMLESSLY THROUGH GOLDEN NATIONAL PARK. WE DON'T EXPECT TO HEAR FROM THEM FOR A LONG, LONG TIME. BUT THEN AGAIN, A LONG, LONG TIME IS RELATIVE ISN'T IT?

MORAL OF THE STORY:
KIDS WILL EAT VEGETABLES AND HEALTHY FOODS, IF COOKED PROPERLY.

AT CHEFABLES, WE'RE CONSTANTLY CREATING TASTY NEW RECIPES TO INTRODUCE KIDS TO THE JOY OF VEGETABLES (FRUITS AND WHOLE GRAINS, TOO).

An Urban Fairy Tale

Trevor was a happy boy who loved climbing trees, playing with his trains, and riding his trike. Every night for dinner his mom fixed him a delicious meal made from the yummiest foods around. But he sat at the table alone while his mother was working, his brother was texting, and his father was golfing.

No matter what she made, Trevor never seemed to eat much. Trevor's mom begged him to eat more. She cooked more and more of his favorite foods. But nothing worked.

She went searching for answers.

She surfed the web, polled her mommy's group, consulted her yoga instructor, and even joined a culinary support group.

But, there were no answers...until one day, while emptying the dishwasher, a genie appeared.

"I grant you three fishes," he bellowed.

"Three wishes you mean," she responded.

"What?" he said.

"Three wishes, you mean," she repeated in a louder voice.

Well, after some pretty heated negotiations (the mom was a lawyer) they settled for two wishes and one fish.

The first wish was for a recipe so yummy that her little boy would eat more; the second wish was for a new blender; and for the third…she asked for a large, dayboat, line caught, wild salmon.

With a single poof everything appeared on the kitchen counter. She quickly picked up the recipe and studied it.

Much to her dismay, it looked like any ordinary recipe except at the bottom it said to make sure you eat this meal with the whole family.

That night she followed the recipe exactly and served the meal to the entire family. Trevor ate everything on his plate and even begged for seconds. As for the wild salmon...well that's an even bigger fish tale.

Moral of the story: children like to eat with people and when they do, they eat better and try new things. Food behaviors are largely influenced by parents, family members, and caregivers.

Chefables often serves its meals family style so kids eat together and learn from each other.

A Very Short Tale

Once upon a time there was a Mother Duck (who by the way was no relation to Mother Goose.) But, she did love to eat. One day, she and a hungry caterpillar went out for a nutritious lunch of fruit and vegetables, grains, and proteins. The next day the caterpillar was gone but Mother Duck kept on eating.

She dined with the boy who ate everything, the witch who
lived in the gingerbread house and, of course, the frog prince.
Then one night these three little pigs came over for supper.

Now, the first little pig wouldn't eat any vegetables,
the second little pig gorged on carbohydrates, and the
third pig, well, he only ate sugar.

Mother Duck had never seen anything like it before.
These little pigs were acting like pigs. Didn't they know that
in order to stay relevant in today's media drenched, socially
connected, fast paced, attention deficit defining generation
you need to eat a variety of healthy food? What...
did they miss that day at fairy tale school?
Luckily, a hungry wolf stopped by.

The End

Moral of the story: to develop
lasting good eating habits,
young children need to eat
the right balance of foods,
in the right quantities.

At Chefables we create portions that
are just the right size for children so
that they learn to eat a balanced meal
that covers all the important food groups.

Postscript: No actual pigs were harmed during the writing of this story. Although the thought of a B.L.T. did cross our minds.

A Little Take Out Philosophy

In the mixed up world of Socratese, the philosopher sock puppet, and Professor Swinestine, the brilliant mathematician and stuffed pig, nothing was as it seems. The grass wasn't green, the sky wasn't blue, and gravity wasn't relative. The past was the present. And the future was hearsay. It was a world where verbs masqueraded as nouns. And adjectives acted like adverbs. But, that's enough pre-amble. You probably want to get to the meat of the story. So here we go.

It all started at the Fussy Eaters Academy Awards dinner.

The first award of the night went to Maya for the year's most convincing "I don't like carrots anymore" performance.

Next, Jake won for refusing all his fruit…all the time. And, for the most dramatic whole grains inspired temper tantrum, the award went to David.

Of course, the lifetime diva award went to Alyssa for convincing her parents that the only thing she would eat without a fight was a grilled cheese sandwich. It was quite a night…there were plates and plates of uneaten vegetables, bowls of untouched fruit, baskets of beautiful whole grains, celebrity sightings, and a musical performance by the Taste Buds.

However, this year was special. You see, the Academy was introducing an exciting new category called "I'll try healthier foods for a change." The audience members were both intrigued and skeptical. In a word, they were intreptical (which according to fairy tale lexicon is in fact a word.)

But, it wasn't until Lucy gave her acceptance speech for her performance as a vegged up, happy go lucky, natural foods explorer that things got really interesting.

She started by thanking her parents for their continued support and for exposing her to new foods. Then she spoke of her upcoming role as a peas loving, carrot crunching activist. "This role will require me to eat heaps of whole grains, organic vegetables, and fruits rich in antioxidants. It's the healthiest opportunity I've ever gotten. I hope I can do it."

The crowd went bananas (literally) and gave her a standing ovation. And then, like any awards ceremony worth its weight in salt, they broke for a commercial.

Moral of the Story: Don't encourage fussy eating or opting out of nutritious foods like vegetables, fruits, and whole grains.

Chefables encourages children to try new and nutritious foods because good nutrition in the early years impacts them for a lifetime.

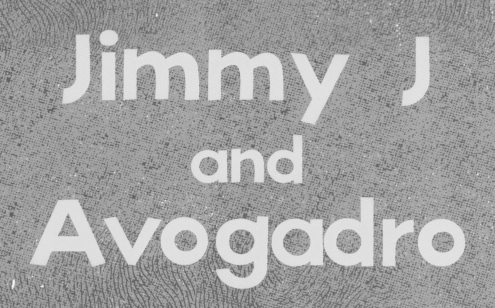

Jimmy J
and
Avogadro

In the genius world of Jimmy J
only two things really mattered...
his secret lab and his pet mole,
Avogadro, (who was also a
crime-fighting, number crunching
super secret agent.)

Now, Jimmy J was a very curious child who was always asking lots of questions like: why do things float, what makes things fall, and why does his sister have so many temper tantrums during mealtime? To find the answers Jimmy J went to his secret lab and started experimenting.

Well, it didn't take long for Jimmy J to figure out that the Archimedes Principle made things float and gravity made things fall. But, understanding the underlying principle of the temper tantrum was a far more complicated problem. One that would require advanced technology.

So, he did what any genius child would do, he downloaded the most powerful app he could find onto his iBanana 4+1 GS gaming device. In seconds, he had an answer.

He learned that kids' tastes change as precipitously and unpredictably as this story. Some days they might really like a food and the next day they can't stand it. But Jimmy J wasn't satisfied. He needed more answers.

That's when Avogadro suggested he try his newest invention, the Burplitz 6.022 that translates temper tantrums into plain and simple English.

Jimmy J eagerly typed in "I DON'T WANT ANY PEAS TODAY" which his sister had screamed last night at dinner. This short, seemingly straightforward sentence translated into an unexpectedly long and unwieldy one. Here's what the Burplitz spit out:

I AM NOT IN THE MOOD TODAY. I DON'T KNOW WHY. AND IF YOU TRY AND MAKE ME EAT PEAS IT WILL MAKE ME MAD. BUT, I DON'T WANT YOU TO THINK THIS MEANS THAT I MIGHT NOT WANT PEAS TOMORROW. OR, THAT I MIGHT NEVER WANT TO SEE A PEA AGAIN. IF YOU DO THAT IT WILL MAKE ME REALLY MAD. REMEMBER, I'M JUST A LITTLE GIRL TRYING TO FIGURE OUT THE CONCEPT OF PREFERENCE, WHICH ALREADY EXCEEDS MY SYLLABLE LIMIT BY A FACTOR OF TWO. AND THAT MAKES ME REALLY, REALLY MAD.

Wow, Jimmy J couldn't believe it.
He finally understood the fundamental basis
for his sister's unexplained eating habits not to
mention disruptive temper tantrums. **This was big.**
We're talking gastronomically big.

Armed with this valuable data Jimmy J could eliminate
his sister's temper tantrums, improve her eating habits,
relieve his parents of enormous nutritionally induced
stress, and who knows maybe even take over the
world—which is what any self respecting
genius child would want to do.

And that brings us thankfully,
to the end of this story.

MORAL OF THE STORY:
WHEN KIDS SAY "NO",
IT MAY NOT MEAN "NO"
FOREVER. TRY, TRY AGAIN.

At Chefables we
understand the "preference
issue," distinguishing between
a true dislike and a desire on
any given day. That's why
we continually expose children
to new foods and work with
families and caregivers to
also do the same.

The chicken
and
the Acorn

Once upon a time there was
a little chicken famous throughout
the land for always eating everything
on her plate. Her parents were so proud.
They were sure that one day their
little bundle of yellowness would
be a big strong hen.

And it was true. She was growing so tall that her friends started calling her Chicken Not So Little. Day after day, Chicken Not So Little cleaned her plate. Except for one day when Chicken Not So Little was not so hungry.

She had gone to the Henny Penny Cafe for lunch. But, when Henny asked what she wanted, Chicken Not So Little replied, "Oh, I'm not so hungry today. I think I will pass." Chicken Not So Little's mom was concerned. Something must be wrong, she thought.

Well, right about that time, in a case of unbelievable serendipity... the kind you can only find in fairy tales, the sky began to fall and with it what looked like a giant acorn but what was in fact a small acorn just really close up.

At any rate, after falling, the acorn got up and shook himself off while muttering something not so nice about oak trees. He was a self-described curmudgeon, which is much more fun to say than to spell.

He marched right up to Chicken Not So Little's mom and said, "Don't fret, kids change their food intake all the time. Some days they eat lots...like if they are growing. And other days they may nibble very lightly. It's nothing to worry about. Just keep feeding them healthy foods. And all will be well." And it was. Because a fallen acorn never lies.

Moral of the story:
don't worry, childrens' food
intake can change on a daily basis.

At chefables, we understand that kids eat voraciously on high-activity days and selectively on other days. Regardless of their appetites, we always serve them nutritional, well-balanced, and delicious meals.

Parker and his
Fairy Godfather

Parker and his Fairy Godfather

Parker was very competitive. He loved being the fastest, the smartest and the funniest kid on the block. And, he was...except when it came to eating everything on his plate.

You see his mom liked to pile his plate up with lots of food. Like last night, she served him a mountain of potatoes, a tower of green beans, and a heap of turkey. He tried and tried to eat it all, but he just couldn't do it.

Poor little Parker was so sad.
He went back to his room to sulk. It just
didn't make sense. He could do other things...
why not this? It's just not fair, he thought.

Then, without warning, his fairy godfather
appeared to him. "Whatsa matta you?
Why you looka so sad?" he asked.

Parker explained his situation and asked for
help. The fairy godfather explained, (off
the record of course), that a kid's stomach
wasn't as big as many adults thought. In fact,
kids tummies are very small. That's why you
only need small servings of food. And with a
bada boom, bada bing the fairy godfather
disappeared into a puff of cannoli smoke.

Moral of the Story: Kids don't need to eat as much as we think they do.

At Chefables, we recognize that recommended serving sizes for kids are not
the same as for older children or adults. By serving age-appropriate portions
we're building a foundation for long-term healthy lifestyles.

ONCE UPON A TIME THERE WAS A SMALL WOLF WHO LOVED GETTING HIS WAY...ESPECIALLY AT MEALTIME. EVERY NIGHT WHEN HIS MOM WOULD BRING HIM A PLATE OF DELICIOUS NUTRITIOUS FOODS, WITH A SIDE OF FRESH ORGANIC VEGETABLES, HE WOULD FIND SOMETHING TO COMPLAIN ABOUT. ONE NIGHT SHE GAVE HIM SWEET CORN ON THE COB AND HE SAID: "**BOY**, I HATE CORN. I'M NOT GOING TO EAT THIS. CAN YOU GIVE ME A COOKIE INSTEAD? I PROMISE TO EAT MY VEGETABLES TOMORROW NIGHT." SO, THE NEXT NIGHT, INSTEAD OF CORN, SHE GAVE HIM CARROTS AND WHAT DID THE WOLF DO? HE SAID, "**BOY** OH **BOY**. CARROTS.. UGH. I HATE CARROTS. CAN I HAVE A COOKIE INSTEAD? I PROMISE TO EAT MY VEGETABLES TOMORROW NIGHT."

AND SO THE NEXT NIGHT SHE GAVE HIM GREEN BEANS, AND ONCE AGAIN HE BROKE HIS PROMISE. PRETTY SOON, THE ONLY THINGS THE WOLF WOULD EAT AS A SIDE DISH WERE COOKIES AND THAT MADE HIM LESS THAN HEALTHY AND HIS MOM MORE THAN UNHAPPY.

THAT'S WHEN HIS MOTHER, A NOTED REVERSE PSYCHOLOGIST, DECIDED TO PUT HER KNOWLEDGE TO GOOD USE.

SO, THE NEXT NIGHT SHE GAVE HER SON A PLATE PILED HIGH WITH COOKIES. FIRST, HE STARED AT IT. NEXT, HE POKED AT IT. AND, THEN MUCH TO HIS OWN SURPRISE, HE ASKED HIS MOM FOR A PLATE OF PEAS AND CORN INSTEAD. BUT SHE SAID: "I'M SORRY SON, I ONLY HAVE COOKIES LEFT. I GAVE ALL THE VEGETABLES AWAY SINCE YOU NEVER LIKED THEM." "BOY, MOM," HE CRIED. "DOES THAT MEAN I'M NOT GOING TO GET VEGETABLES EVER AGAIN? I'M STILL YOUNG. I STILL HAVE TIME TO DEVELOP GOOD HABITS. REALLY. I PROMISE JUST GIVE ME ANOTHER CHANCE."

AND THROUGH A TWIST OF FATE NOT UNLIKE WHAT HAPPENS IN LEGITIMATE FAIRY TALES AND PROFESSIONAL WRESTLING, THE WOLF GOT HIS WISH. BECAUSE SUDDENLY, COMPLETE WITH A LIGHT BULB GOING OFF IN A THOUGHT BUBBLE ABOVE HER HEAD... THE MOM SAID, "WAIT, I HAVE AN IDEA. WHY DON'T YOU GO NEXT DOOR AND SEE IF OUR NEIGHBORS HAVE ANY VEGETABLES TO SHARE." SO THE HUNGRY LITTLE WOLF WENT TO THE NEIGHBOR'S HOUSE. HE KNOCKED ON THE DOOR AND MUCH TO HIS SURPRISE THREE LITTLE PIGS ANSWERED.

MORAL OF THE STORY:
DON'T OFFER ALTERNATIVE MEALS WHEN A CHILD REFUSES TO EAT.

AT CHEFABLES WE PROVIDE A HEALTHY VARIETY OF FOOD AT EACH MEAL, KNOWING THAT SOMETIMES CHILDREN WILL REFUSE. PATIENCE, DILIGENCE AND CONSTANT EXPOSURE ARE ESSENTIAL. WE WORK WITH TEACHERS AND CAREGIVERS TO PROVIDE POSITIVE REINFORCEMENT AND LEARNING TECHNIQUES TO ENCOURAGE KIDS TO EXPAND THEIR HEALTHY FOOD REPERTOIRE.

the End

Meet the Taste Buds

Once there were 5 little kids:

Sally Sweet

Sam Sour

Bobby Bitter

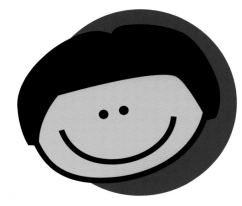

Ulysses Umami

Serena Salty

They were best buds. They did everything together...

...play in the park. Climb trees. Have sleepovers. Mostly though they liked having adventures in the kitchen. But, it didn't start out that way.

You see, a long time ago, when Sally, Bobby, Sam, Serena, and Ulysses were much younger they didn't get along that well. It's just that they had very different tastes. Sally liked sweet things, Bobby preferred bitter, Sam wanted sour, Serena loved salt, and Ulysses was totally into umami.

Everyday, at lunchtime, Sally would turn her nose up at Serena's food shrieking: "ewww, what is that? It looks disgusting." Bobby did the same thing to Ulysses. Sam did it to Serena. And so on and so forth. Pretty soon, lunchtime was filled with a chorus of ewws and ugghs. Each kid turning his or her nose up at what the other was eating. Of course, none of this encouraged good eating habits.

GROSS

But all that changed when they met wise old Chef Able in aisle 3 of the local super market. He overheard them arguing about what to buy for lunch. "May I introduce myself? I'm Chef Able, culinary wizard and intrepid epicurian explorer. And I'm here to help." Then he pulled out his magic whisk, waved it in the air three times and chanted the following spell:

Yrrah rettop sekil lessurb stuorps

Yrrah rettop sekil lessurb stuorps

Yrrah rettop sekil lessurb stuorps

I'M NOT EATING IT!

POOF!

The whole gang was transported to his very gourmet, super sweet, all tricked out kitchen. And that's really where this culinary adventure begins. Because from this point on, Chef Able pulled out all the stops and showed these kids how to combine flavors like sour and sweet or bitter and umami.

He created taste sensations these kids had never even imagined. He even let them study his recipe books that were filled with all kinds of culinary secrets. The kids couldn't believe their eyes or their taste buds.

Then a buzzer went off.

"Wow, look at the time," Chef Able remarked. "Drats (which is Wizard talk for oops) I've got to go and prepare for my meeting with the spice sisters." Once again he pulled out his magic whisk and started muttering these lines:

Basilum, clovus, dillum

Cuminus, curryum, mustardus

Saffronum, sageus, marjoram

POOF!

The kids were back in aisle 3. But this time they weren't arguing. In fact, they couldn't wait to buy a variety of foods, to experiment with new flavors and to try new combinations. And that's where this culinary adventure ends.

Moral of the story: start teaching kids about healthy eating when they're young because that's when they're strongly influenced by good taste and peer pressure.

Chefables is helping kids cultivate strong eating habits that will last a lifetime by providing nutritional, well-balanced and delicious meals.

Vegetables Have Feelings, Too

Once upon a time there was a little girl named Gretel (no, not the one you're thinking about and no, she did not have a sweet tooth or a desire to go on long hikes through the forest). But she did have an amazing vegetable garden in her backyard.

Every day she went to her garden and grabbed a bunch of snap peas to eat. Day after day she went to the garden and always picked snap peas. She would look at the other vegetables but just wasn't interested. No reason. Just not interested.

But all was not well in the garden.

While the snap peas were getting all the attention, the rest of the vegetables were feeling left out. In fact, several of the carrots found themselves in a mixed vegetable self-help group.

Every week they would share their inner most feelings. The onions mostly cried. The asparagus felt rejected. The eggplant was having an identity crisis. The celery was hitting the ranch dressing pretty hard. And the cucumber had begun drowning her sorrows in vinegar (and between you and me, she was practically pickled).

The group leader, a Freudian vegan, told them not to blame themselves. He reminded them that they were all full of good vitamins and minerals. "It's just that kids' taste buds need time to develop," he said. "You need to be patient...and that's all we have time for today."

A few weeks passed without any changes. And then one cold crisp sunny morning, Gretel walked right by the snap peas and went to the carrots and pulled one out. From that day forward the carrots were happy. Of course, the snap peas were now attending self-help meetings twice a week.

Moral of the story: kids eating habits change over time. You just need to be patient.

Chefables is very patient with kids because we understand their ever-changing eating habits. Cultivating good eating habits early on is critical to healthy development and growth.

RaVeL

ONCE UPON A TIME, IN A LAND FAR, FAR AWAY THERE WAS
A HANDSOME KING AND A BEAUTIFUL QUEEN WHO LIVED IN A
PEACEFUL KINGDOM. WELL, IT CAME TO PASS THAT THE QUEEN
GAVE BIRTH TO A GORGEOUS BABY GIRL WITH GIANT BLUE EYES,
CURLY RED HAIR, AND A PERFECTLY SHAPED UPTURNED
NOSE. THEY NAMED HER RAVEL. SHE WAS A HAPPY BABY.

SHE LOVED PLAYING IN THE ROYAL PLAYGROUND WITH
HER TODDLER FRIENDS, RIDING HER ROYAL PONIES,
AND ORDERING HER ROYAL SUBJECTS AROUND. IT
WAS A JOYOUS TIME. EVERYONE IN THE KINGDOM
WAS FILLED WITH HAPPINESS AND HOPE.

BUT ONE DAY, A BITTER WITCH, DISGUISED AS A 1% MILK MAIDEN, CAST A *SPELL* ON PRINCESS RAVEL. UNDER HER EVIL *SPELL* RAVEL WOULD EAT ONE THING AND ONE THING ONLY—ROYAL O'S. WHEN RAVEL WAS SHOWN NEW FOODS SHE WOULD SCREAM, CRY AND UNRAVEL. THIS MADE THE KING AND QUEEN AND EVERYONE IN THE KINGDOM VERY, VERY SAD. PRETTY SOON THE KINGDOM WAS NO LONGER A HAPPY, PEACEFUL PLACE.

SO THE KING DID WHAT ANY WISE KING WOULD DO: HE ISSUED AN EDICT DECLARING THAT WHOMEVER COULD BREAK THE *SPELL* WOULD GET A BIG BAG OF GOLD AND A ROYAL PURPLE CAR WITH FANCY WHEELS, POWER WINDOWS AND HEATED SEATS.

PEOPLE CAME FROM ALL OVER THE LAND IN HOPES OF BREAKING
THE EVIL SPELL. WIZARDS TRIED TO TRICK HER. SOOTHSAYERS
TRIED TO SOOTHE HER. LADIES IN WAITING WAITED AND
WAITED. BUT, NO ONE SUCCEEDED. AND, THE
KINGDOM FELL INTO DISREPAIR.

BUT ONE FOGGY DAY, THE FOOD COURT JESTER SHOWED UP WITH A BUSHEL
OF APPLES. HE TOLD THE KING AND QUEEN IF THEY LET HIM FEED RAVEL
HIS APPLES FOR THE NEXT 7 TO 11 DAYS HE WOULD BREAK THE SPELL.
THE KING AND QUEEN SKEPTICALLY AGREED.

ON THE FIRST DAY, THE FOOD COURT JESTER PREPARED A CINNAMON
APPLESAUCE, WHICH RAVEL PROMPTLY SPIT AT HIM. THE SECOND DAY,
HE TRIED GREEN APPLE SLAW, WHICH SHE THREW TO THE FLOOR. THE THIRD,
FOURTH, FIFTH, SIXTH, SEVENTH, EIGHTH, NINTH, AND TENTH DAYS WERE THE
SAME. BUT ON THE 11TH DAY SHE TOOK A BITE OF HIS BAKED APPLE ROYALE
AND SMILED.

THE KINGDOM WAS SAVED. AND THE FOOD COURT JESTER DROVE OFF WITH
HIS BAG OF GOLD. WORD IS HE USED HIS MONEY TO OPEN A CHAIN OF APPLE
STORES IN SOMETHING HE CALLED A MALL.

The End

Our Team Who Helped Us Put This Book Together

Marcus Cutler — A Little Take Out Philosophy

Marcus Cutler has always loved drawing and being creative but being an illustrator wasn't his very first ambition in life. He's not too worried though because being a stunt man would have been much too dangerous anyway. www.marcuscutler.com

Lloyd Dangle — The Adventures of Captain Carotene

Dangle's comics and illustrations have appeared in over one hundred magazines and newspapers. His comic strip Troubletown has been a popular feature in the alternative press since 1988. He also illustrated the packaging for the world's most popular cold remedy, Airborne. http://blog.troubletown.com

Mike Eustis — The Chicken and the Acorn

Mike Eustis is a Children's Illustrator based in Sunny Seattle. When he's not working in the studio with his large boned cat, Adam, you'll find Mike bird watching, cooking and napping on the docks of Lake Union. www.mikeeustis.com

David Habben — About Us

Born in Oregon, raised in Idaho and educated in Utah and California, Habben has been drawing as long as he can remember. Encouraged by family and friends, he has pursued art throughout his educational, professional and personal life. His work has been included in a wide variety of venues and publications throughout the U.S. www.habbenink.com

Christine Hale — The Rule of Thumb

Christine Hale is an American illustrator that loves to draw and eat food. She also loves to make music and make art for music, like: posters and album artwork for bands. Pretty much drawing, eating, and music are her favorite things. Also, peonies, traveling to new places, sunny days, laughing, and funny dogs. www.lovechristine.com

Melissa Hutton — The Taste Buds

Melissa Hutton is a graphic designer, artist and illustrator in San Francisco. She lives in a yellow house on a hill, has a cat named Olive and her favorite taste bud is sweet. Her art has been displayed in both solo and group expositions around the country and she is currently represented by The Hespe Gallery in San Francisco. In addition to illustrating The Taste Buds, Melissa also art directed every morsel of Chef Able's Fables. www.melissahutton.com

The Imagineering Company — Chef Able's Fables

Julie and Susan (or Susan and Julie) are part of the writing team who added the sizzle to the fables in Chef Able's Fables. When they are not writing mouth watering tales with nutritious morals they are crafting clever prose, names, and taglines. www.imagineeringsf.com

Erik Krenz — An Urban Fairy Tale

Erik Krenz was born and raised in Minneapolis, MN. He got his BFA from the Minneapolis College of Art and Design and is now working as a freelance illustrator. If he's not working, then he loves to run, and hang out with his girlfriend and friends. He collects old photos and fossils, and makes a mean chicken curry. www.erikbkrenz.com

Alyssa Nassner — Ravel

Baltimore native now living and illustrating full time in the beautiful city of Philadelphia, Alyssa spent her childhood drawing animals, and reading Harry Potter books. She now dabbles in cartooning, screen printing, and pattern design and strives to create work that is fun, imaginative, and colorful! Currently she spends her free time running her own business, Small Talk Studio, learning to cook, and playing with her puppy, Sully. www.alyssanassner.com

Sirron Norris — The Wolf Who Cried Boy

Born in Cleveland, Ohio, Sirron graduated from the Art Institute of Pittsburgh, before settling down in San Francisco in 1997. Since his arrival he has been busy. In 2002 he was the recipient of the prestigious Wattis Artist in Residence from the Yerba Buena Center for the Arts. His most notable mural, "Victorion: El Defensor de la Mission" located in the historic "Balmy Alley" has been featured in several magazines, books and advertisements. In 2010 Norris opened his art studio & gallery in the Mission district where he offer arts for the family and hopes to serve as an inspiration to up and coming artists. www.sirronnorris.com

Ian Phillips — Jimmy J and Avogadro

Ian Phillips is an award-winning illustrator based in Toronto Canada, although he can frequently be seen wandering up and down Ocean Beach in San Francisco. He likes to draw pictures of candy floss and ice cream, but he is an avid cook and his favorite dish is a steaming bowl of green peas. www.pasdechance.com

Anna Tillett — Parker and His Fairy Godfather

Anna Tillett is the one man (lady) band and art making machine of Anna Tillett Designs. Tillett's illustrative style is continually influenced by her long time infatuation with 1950's and 1960's illustration. Love of word play, pop culture nostalgia, and childhood wonder is a constant presence in her work. You can currently find Anna working on the next goofy idea in her California studio where music is constantly playing. She talks to her parents twice a week and tries to eat her veggies. www.annatillettdesigns.com

Michelle White — Vegetables Have Feelings, Too

Michelle "Milo" is a Bay Area freelance illustrator who is passionate about the simple art of drawing. She has a unique vision of the world around her and shares her thoughts in sometimes startlingly honest ways. Her work often has a hint of twisted humor. www.michelle-white.com

Phoenix Zoellick — A Very Short Tale

A freelance artist and illustrator living in San Francisco, Zoellick loves subtle references and secret codes, drawing continuous inspiration from tattoos, religious iconography and fairy tales. "I see it as passing notes to you in the big classroom of life; I love it when you get it, and giggle at our little inside jokes." www.pixiebird.com